THE USBORNE CHILDREN'S SONGBOOK

Compiled by Heather Amery
Illustrated by Stephen Cartwright

Music arrangements by Barrie Carson Turner

Music setting by Richard Dawson Music Engraving

There are some little yellow ducks to spot in this book.

How many can you find?

First published in 1988 by Usborne Publishing Ltd., 20 Garrick Street, London WC2E 9BJ, England

© Usborne Publishing Ltd. 1988

The name Usborne and the device 🎈 are Trade Marks of Usborne Publishing Ltd.

Contents

4 Here we go round the mulberry bush
6 One, two, three, four, five
7 Little Bo-Peep
8 If you're happy
9 Where, oh where has my little dog gone?
10 Ten in a bed
12 Twinkle, twinkle little star
14 Old MacDonald had a farm
16 I had a little nut tree
17 Frère Jacques
18 Nick nack paddy wack
20 Sing a song of sixpence
22 Jingle bells
24 Michael Finnigan
26 I saw three ships
27 Yankee Doodle
28 London Bridge is falling down
30 Pop goes the weasel
31 The grand old Duke of York
32 One more river
34 Click go the shears
36 My bonnie lies over the ocean
38 She'll be coming round the mountain
40 There's a big ship sailing
42 Cockles and mussels
44 Over the hills and far away
46 Au clair de la lune
48 Aiken Drum
50 Strawberry Fair
52 Oh, Susanna
54 Michael, row the boat ashore
56 A froggy went a-courting
58 Home, home on the range
60 Donkey riding
62 Lewis wedding song
64 Index of first lines

Here we go round the mulberry bush

1   Here we go round the mulberry bush,
The mulberry bush, the mulberry bush,
Here we go round the mulberry bush
On a cold and frosty morning.

2   This is the way we clap our hands,
Clap our hands, clap our hands,
This is the way we clap our hands
On a cold and frosty morning.

3   This is the way we wash our clothes,
Wash our clothes, wash our clothes,
This is the way we wash our clothes
On a cold and frosty morning.

4   This is the way we sweep the floor,
Sweep the floor, sweep the floor,
This is the way we sweep the floor
On a cold and frosty morning.

You can make up more verses of your own of things you can do, like comb your hair, brush your teeth and wash your face.

One, two, three, four, five

One, two, three, four, five,
Once I caught a fish alive;
Six, seven, eight, nine, ten,
Then I let it go again.

Why did you let it go?
Because it bit my finger so.
Which finger did it bite?
This little finger on the right.

Little Bo-Peep

1. Lit-tle Bo-peep, she lost her sheep And did-n't know where to find them; Leave them a - lone and they'll come home, And bring their tails be-hind them. hind them. tail.

1 Little Bo-Peep she lost her sheep
And didn't know where to find them.
Leave them alone, and they'll come home,
And bring their tails behind them.

2 It happened one day, as Bo-Peep did stray
Into a meadow hard by,
There she espied their tails side by side,
All hung on a tree to dry.

3 She heaved a sigh, and wiped her eye
And ran over hill and dale, O!
And tried what she could,
    as a shepherdess should,
To tack to each sheep its tail, O!

7

If you're happy

1 If you're happy and you know it, clap your hands.
   If you're happy and you know it, clap your hands.
   If you're happy and you know it,
   Then you'll surely want to show it,
   If you're happy and you know it, clap your hands.

2 If you're happy and you know it, nod your head . . .

More verses to sing: 3 If you're happy and you know it, stamp your feet . . .
4 If you're happy and you know it, say "Ha! Ha!" . . .
5 If you're happy and you know it, do all four! . . .

Where, oh where has my little dog gone

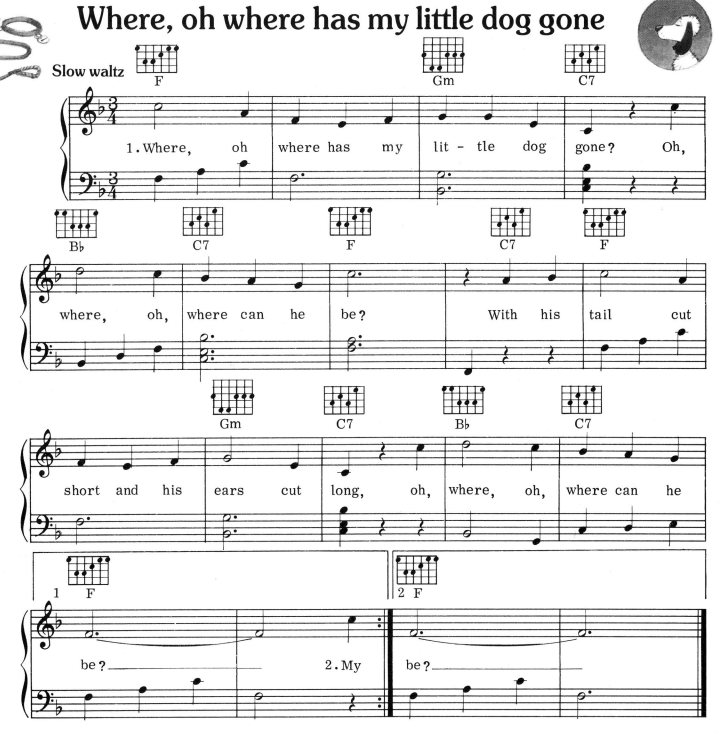

Slow waltz

1. Where, oh where has my lit-tle dog gone? Oh,
where, oh, where can he be? With his tail cut
short and his ears cut long, oh, where, oh, where can he

1 F
be? _____

2. My

2 F
be? _____

1   Where, oh where has my little dog gone?
Oh, where, oh, where can he be?
With his tail cut short and his ears cut long,
Oh, where, oh, where can he be?

2   My little dog always waggles his tail
Whenever he wants his grog.
And if the tail were more strong than he,
Why, the tail would waggle the dog.

9

Ten in a bed

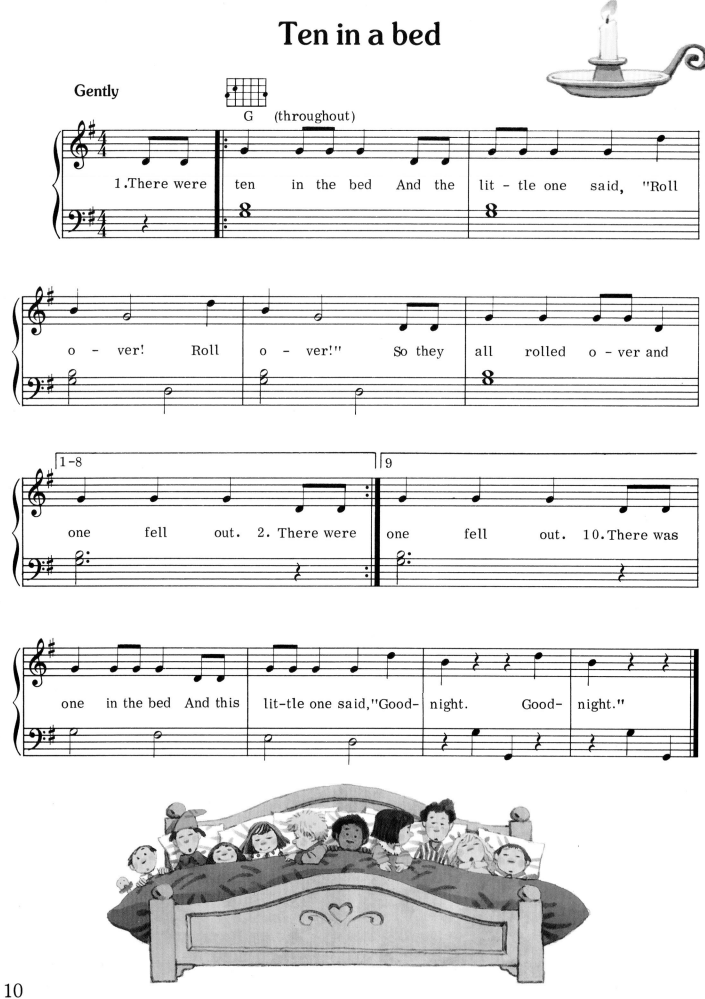

Gently

G (throughout)

1. There were ten in the bed And the lit-tle one said, "Roll

o - ver! Roll o - ver!" So they all rolled o - ver and

1-8 | one fell out. 2. There were | 9 | one fell out. 10. There was

one in the bed And this lit-tle one said, "Good-night. Good-night."

1   There were ten in the bed
    And the little one said,
    "Roll over! Roll over!"
    So they all rolled over and one fell out.

2   There were nine in the bed
        And the little one said . . .

3   There were eight in the bed
        And the little one said . . .

4   There were seven in the bed
        And the little one said . . .

5   There were six in the bed
        And the little one said . . .

6   There were five in the bed
        And the little one said . . .

7   There were four in the bed
        And the little one said . . .

8   There were three in the bed
        And the little one said . . .

9   There were two in the bed
        And the little one said . . .

10 There was one in the bed
    And this little one said,
    "Good night. Good night."

Twinkle, twinkle, little star

Gently

D   G   D   Em   D

1. Twin - kle, twin - kle,   lit - tle star,   How I won - der

A7   D   Em7   A7   D   A   D   Em7   A7

what you are,   Up a - bove the   world so   high,   Like a dia - mond

D   A7   D   G   D

in the   sky.   Twin - kle,   twin - kle   lit - tle star,

Em   D   1-3 A7   D   4 A7   D

How I won - der   what you are.   what you are.

12

1   Twinkle, twinkle, little star,
     How I wonder what you are,
     Up above the world so high,
     Like a diamond in the sky.

        Twinkle, twinkle, little star,
        How I wonder what you are.

2   When the blazing sun is gone,
     When he nothing shines upon,
     Then you show your little light,
     Twinkle, twinkle, all the night.
        Twinkle, twinkle, little star . . .

3   Then the traveller in the dark
     Thanks you for your tiny spark;
     Could he see which way to go
     If you did not twinkle so?
        Twinkle, twinkle, little star . . .

4   In the dark blue sky you keep,
     While you through my curtains peep,
     And you never shut your eye
     Till the sun is in the sky.
        Twinkle, twinkle, little star . . .

Old MacDonald had a farm

1   Old MacDonald had a farm, E.I.E.I.O.
    And on this farm he had some chicks, E.I.E.I.O.
    With a chick-chick here and a chick-chick there,
    Here a chick, there a chick, everywhere a chick-chick.
    Old MacDonald had a farm, E.I.E.I.O.

2   Old MacDonald had a farm, E.I.E.I.O.
    And on this farm he had some ducks, E.I.E.I.O.
    With a quack-quack here and a quack-quack there,
    Here a quack, there a quack, everywhere a quack-quack.
    Old MacDonald had a farm, E.I.E.I.O.

3   Old MacDonald had a farm, E.I.E.I.O.
    And on this farm he had some sheep, E.I.E.I.O.
    With a baa-baa here and a baa-baa there,
    Here a baa, there a baa, everywhere a baa-baa.
    Old MacDonald had a farm, E.I.E.I.O.

4   Old MacDonald had a farm, E.I.E.I.O.
    And on this farm he had some pigs, E.I.E.I.O.
    With a grunt-grunt here and a grunt-grunt there,
    Here a grunt, there a grunt, everywhere a grunt-grunt.
    Old MacDonald had a farm, E.I.E.I.O.

You can make up more verses of your own about other animals you can think of and the noises they make.

I had a little nut tree

I had a little nut tree, nothing would it bear
But a silver nutmeg and a golden pear;
The King of Spain's daughter came to visit me,
And all for the sake of my little nut tree.
I skipped over water, I danced over sea,
And all the birds in the air couldn't catch me.

Frère Jacques

Steadily  F (throughout)

Frè - re Jac - ques, frè - re Jac - ques, dor - mez-

vous, dor - mez - vous? Son - nez les ma-

-ti - nes, son - nez les ma - ti - nes, Din din

1. **2.**

don! Din din don! Frè - re don!

Frère Jacques, Frère Jacques,
Dormez-vous? Dormez-vous?
Sonnez les matines,
Sonnez les matines,
Din, din, don! Din, din, don!

17

Nick nack paddy wack

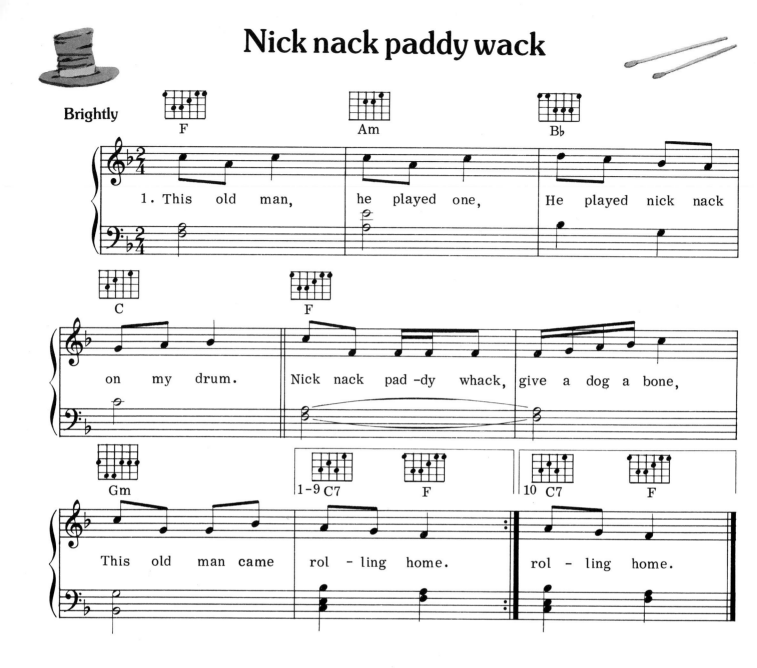

Brightly

F | Am | B♭
C | F |
Gm | 1-9 C7 | F | 10 C7 | F

1. This old man, he played one, | He played nick nack | on my drum. | Nick nack pad -dy whack, | give a dog a bone, | This old man came | rol - ling home. | rol - ling home.

1   This old man, he played one,
    He played nick nack on my drum.
    Nick nack paddy wack, give a dog a bone,
    This old man came rolling home.

18

2   This old man, he played two,
He played nick nack on my shoe.
   Nick nack paddy wack . . .

3   This old man, he played three,
He played nick nack on the tree.
   Nick nack paddy wack . . .

4   This old man, he played four,
He played nick nack on the door.
   Nick nack paddy wack . . .

5   This old man, he played five,
He played nick nack on the hive.
   Nick nack paddy wack . . .

6   This old man, he played six,
He played nick nack picking up sticks.
   Nick nack paddy wack . . .

7   This old man, he played seven,
He played nick nack up to Heaven.
   Nick nack paddy wack . . .

8   This old man, he played eight,
He played nick nack on the gate.
   Nick nack paddy wack . . .

9   This old man, he played nine,
He played nick nack on a line.
   Nick nack paddy wack . .

10 This old man, he played ten,
He played nick nack with the hen.
   Nick nack paddy wack . . .

Sing a song of sixpence

Joyfully

Bb Gm Cm F7

1. Sing a song of six - pence, a pock - et full of rye;

Bb Gm D Gm

Four and twen - ty black - birds baked in a pie:

Bb Cm

When the pie was op - ened the birds be - gan to sing,

Bb Gm 1 F7 Bb 2 F7 Bb

Was-n't that a daint -y dish to | set be-fore the King! | pecked off her nose!

20

Sing a song of sixpence,
A pocket full of rye,
Four and twenty blackbirds
Baked in a pie.

When the pie was opened
The birds began to sing.
Wasn't that a dainty dish
To set before the king!

The king was in his counting-house,
Counting out his money,
The queen was in the parlour,
Eating bread and honey,

The maid was in the garden,
Hanging out the clothes,
When down came a blackbird
And pecked off her nose.

Jingle bells

Dashing through the snow
In a one-horse open sleigh,
O'er the fields we go,
Laughing all the way;
Bells on bob-tail ring,
Making spirits bright;
What fun it is to ride and sing
A sleighing song tonight.

Jingle bells, jingle bells,
Jingle all the way.
Oh what fun it is to ride
In a one-horse open sleigh.
Jingle bells, jingle bells,
Jingle all the way.
Oh what fun it is to ride
In a one-horse open sleigh.

A day or two ago
I thought I'd take a ride
And soon Miss Fannie Bright
Was seated by my side;
The horse was lean and lank,
Misfortune seem'd his lot,
He got into a drifted bank,
And then we got upsot!

Jingle bells, jingle bells,
Jingle all the way.
Oh what fun it is to ride
In a one-horse open sleigh.
Jingle bells, jingle bells,
Jingle all the way.
Oh what fun it is to ride
In a one-horse open sleigh.

Michael Finnigan

1. There was an old man named Michael Finnigan, He grew whiskers on his chin-i-gin, The wind came out and blew them in-a-gin, Poor old Michael Finni-gan, Begin-a-gin. 2. There Finni-gan.

1   There was an old man named Michael Finnigan,
He grew whiskers on his chinigin.
The wind came out and blew them inagin,
Poor old Michael Finnigan (beginagin).

2   There was an old man named Michael Finnigan,
     He kicked up an awful dinigin,
     Because they said he must not singagin,
     Poor old Michael Finnigan (beginagin).

3   There was an old man named Michael Finnigan,
     He went fishing with a pinigin,
     Caught a fish but dropped it inagin,
     Poor old Michael Finnigan (beginagin).

4   There was an old man named Michael Finnigan,
     Climbed a tree and barked his shinigin,
     Took off several yards of skinigin,
     Poor old Michael Finnigan (beginagin).

5   There was an old man named Michael Finnigan,
     He grew fat and he grew thinagin,
     Then he died, and we have to beginagin,
     Poor old Michael Finnigan, Finnigan.

I saw three ships

I saw three ships come sailing by,
Come sailing by, come sailing by,
I saw three ships come sailing by,
On New-Year's day in the morning.

And what do you think was in them then,
Was in them then, was in them then?
And what do you think was in them then,
On New-Year's day in the morning?

Three pretty girls were in them then,
Were in them then, were in them then,
Three pretty girls were in them then,
On New-Year's day in the morning.

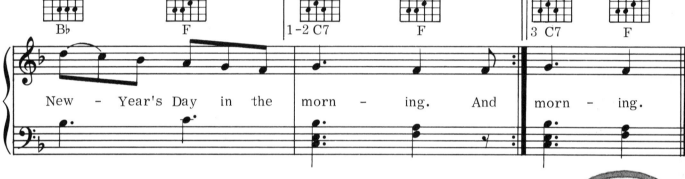

Yankee doodle

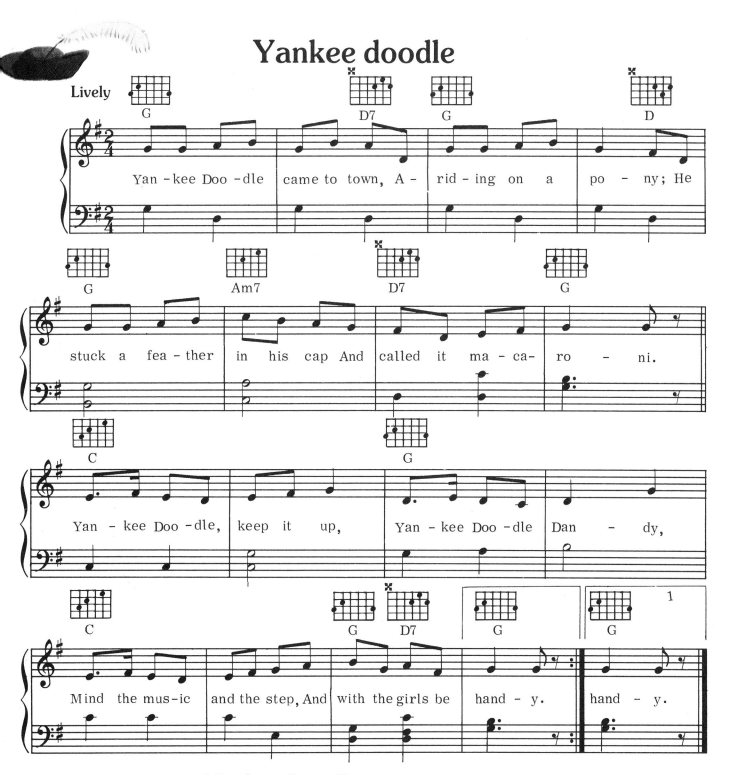

Yankee Doodle came to town,
A-riding on a pony;
He stuck a feather in his cap
And called it macaroni.

Yankee Doodle, keep it up,
Yankee Doodle Dandy,
Mind the music and the step,
And with the girls be handy.

27

London Bridge is falling down

1   London Bridge is falling down,
     Falling down, falling down,
     London Bridge is falling down,
     My fair lady.

2   How shall we build it up again,
     Up again, up again,
     How shall we build it up again,
     My fair lady?

3   Build it up with silver and gold,
     Silver and gold, silver and gold . . .

4   Silver and gold will be stolen away
     Stolen away, stolen away . . .

5   Build it up with wood and clay,
     Wood and clay, wood and clay . . .

6   Wood and clay will wash away,
     Wash away, wash away . . .

7   Build it up with iron and steel,
     Iron and steel, iron and steel . . .

8   Iron and steel will bend and bow,
     Bend and bow, bend and bow . . .

9   Build it up with stone so strong,
     Stone so strong, stone so strong . . .

10 Stone will last for ages long,
     For ages long, for ages long . . .

Pop goes the weasel

Moderately

D A7 D A7 D

Half a pound of tup-pen-ny rice, Half a pound of trea - cle.

A7 D7 G E7 A7 D

Mix it up and make it nice. Pop goes the wea - sel!

Bm Em A Bm Em A

Up and down the Ci - ty Road, In and out the Ea - gle,

G E7 A7 D

That's the way the mo - ney goes. Pop goes the wea - sel!

Half a pound of tuppenny rice,
Half a pound of treacle,
Mix it up and make it nice.
Pop goes the weasel!

Up and down the City Road,
In and out the Eagle,
That's the way the money goes.
Pop goes the weasel!

The grand old Duke of York

Oh, the grand old Duke of York,
He had ten thousand men;
He marched them up to the top of the hill
And he marched them down again.

And when they were up, they were up;
And when they were down, they were down;
And when they were only half way up,
They were neither up nor down.

One more river

With a swing

1. The an-i-mals went in one by one, There's one more ri-ver to cross. The el-e-phant chew-ing a car-ra-way bun There's one more ri-ver to cross. One more ri-ver, and that's the ri-ver of Jor-dan, One more ri-ver, and that's the ri-ver to cross. 2. The cross.

1   The animals went in one by one,
     There's one more river to cross.
     The elephant chewing a carraway bun,
     There's one more river to cross.

     One more river, and that's the river of Jordon
     One more river, and that's the river to cross.

2   The animals went in two by two,
     There's one more river to cross.
     There's the crocodile and the kangaroo,
     There's one more river to cross.
        One more river . . .

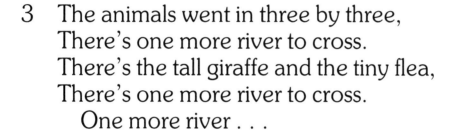

3   The animals went in three by three,
     There's one more river to cross.
     There's the tall giraffe and the tiny flea,
     There's one more river to cross.
        One more river . . .

4   The animals went in four by four,
     There's one more river to cross.
     The big hippopotamus stuck in the door,
     There's one more river to cross.
        One more river . . .

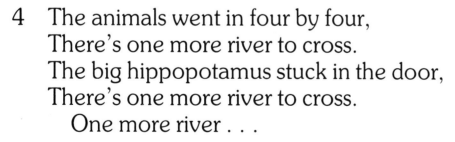

5   The animals went in five by five,
     There's one more river to cross.
     The bees mistook the bear for a hive,
     There's one more river to cross.
        One more river . . .

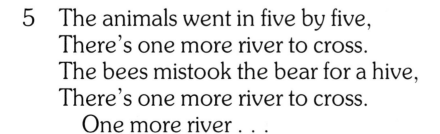

More verses to sing:

6 The monkey was up to his usual tricks . . .   8 Some were early and some were late . . .
7 Said the ant to the antelope,   9 They all formed fours and marched in a line . . .
     "Who are you shovin'?" . . .   10 If you want any more you can sing it again . . .

Click go the shears

With a swing

1. Down by the pen, there the old shear-er stands,
Grasp-ing the shears in his thin bo-ny hands.
Fixed is his gaze on the next sheep to come,
In a lit-tle minute boys, a-no-ther's done.

1   Down by the pen, there the old shearer stands,
    Grasping the shears in his thin bony hands,
    Fixed is his gaze on the next sheep to come,
    In a little minute, boys, another's done.

    Click go the shears, boys, click, click, click.
    Wide is his blow and his hands move so quick.
    The ringer looks around and is beaten by a blow,
    Zip! Another sheep is done and let him go.

2 Out on the floor in his cane bottomed chair,
   There sits the boss with his eyes everywhere,
   Notes well each fleece as it comes to the screen,
   Paying strict attention that it's taken clean.

   Click go the shears, boys, . . .

3 There is the tar-boy awaiting command
   With his black tar pot and his black tarry hands.
   See! One old sheep with a cut on its back.
   Here is what he's waiting for, it's tar here, Jack.

   Click go the shears, boys, . . .

My bonnie lies over the ocean

Not too fast

Bb — Eb — Bb

1. My | bon – nie lies | o –ver the | o –cean, — | My | bon – nie lies

C7 — F — Bb — Eb

o – ver the | sea, — | — | My | bon – nie lies | o – ver the

Bb — Eb — F7 — Bb

o – cean, — | — | Oh | bring back my | bon-nie to | me. — | —

1   My bonnie lies over the ocean,
    My bonnie lies over the sea,
    My bonnie lies over the ocean,
    Oh bring back my bonnie to me.

Bring back, bring back,
Oh bring back my bonnie to me, to me.
Bring back, bring back,
Oh bring back my bonnie to me.

Bring back, bring back, Oh bring back my bon-nie to me, to me.

Bring back, bring back, Oh bring back my bon-nie to me.

1-2 2. Oh

3

2 Oh blow ye winds over the ocean,
   Oh blow ye winds over the sea,
   Oh blow ye winds over the ocean,
   And bring back my bonnie to me.
     Bring back, bring back . . .

3 The winds have blown over the ocean,
   The winds have blown over the sea,
   The winds have blown over the ocean,
   And brought back my bonnie to me.
     Bring back, bring back . . .

She'll be coming round the mountain

1. She'll be coming round the mountain when she comes.
   She'll be coming round the mountain when she comes.
   She'll be coming round the mountain.
   She'll be coming round the mountain.
   She'll be coming round the mountain when she comes.

2. She'll be driving six white horses when she comes.
   She'll be driving six white horses when she comes.
   She'll be driving six white horses.
   She'll be driving six white horses.
   She'll be driving six white horses when she comes.

3. Oh, we'll all go out to greet her when she comes.
   Oh, we'll all go out to greet her when she comes.
   Oh, we'll all go out to greet her.
   Oh, we'll all go out to greet her.
   Oh, we'll all go out to greet her when she comes.

4. But it may be just a while yet 'fore she comes.
   Yes, it may be just a while yet 'fore she comes.
   Oh, it may be just a while yet.
   Yes, it may be just a while yet.
   And it may be just a while yet 'fore she comes.

There's a big ship sailing

Steadily

F

1.There's a big ship sail-ing on the il-ly-al-ly-o, The

F   Dm   G7   C7

il-ly-al-ly-o, the il-ly-al-ly-o, There's a

F   C

big ship sail-ing on the il-ly-al-ly-o,

Bb   C7   F   1-3   4

Heigh-ho, il-ly-al-ly-o. 2.There's a   o.

1   There's a big ship sailing on the illy-ally-o,
    The illy-ally-o, the illy-ally-o,
    There's a big ship sailing on the illy-ally-o,
    Heigh-ho, illy-ally-o.

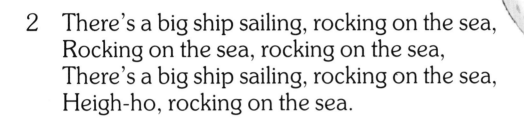

2   There's a big ship sailing, rocking on the sea,
    Rocking on the sea, rocking on the sea,
    There's a big ship sailing, rocking on the sea,
    Heigh-ho, rocking on the sea.

3   The Captain said, "It'll never, never do,
    Never, never do, never, never do."
    The Captain said, "It'll never, never do,
    Heigh-ho, never, never do."

4   The big ship sank to the bottom of the sea,
    The bottom of the sea, the bottom of the sea,
    The big ship sank to the bottom of the sea,
    Heigh-ho, the bottom of the sea.

Cockles and mussels

Waltz time

1. In Dub - lin's fair ci - ty, where girls are so pret - ty, I first set my eyes on sweet Mol - ly Ma - lone, As she wheeled her wheel-bar-row through streets broad and

1   In Dublin's fair city, where girls are so pretty,
I first set my eyes on sweet Molly Malone,
As she wheeled her wheelbarrow through streets broad
     and narrow,
Crying, "Cockles and mussels, alive, alive-o."

Alive, alive-o, alive, alive-o,
Crying, "Cockles and mussels, alive, alive-o."

nar-row, Cry-ing, "Cock-les and mus-sels, a - live, a - live-

-o". A - live, a -live- o,___ a - live, a-live- o,___ Cry-ing

"Cock-les and mus-sels a - live, a - live- o." 2.She o."

2　She was a fishmonger, but it was no wonder,
　For so were her mother and father before,
　And they each wheeled their barrow through streets broad
　　　and narrow,
　Crying, "Cockles and mussels, alive, alive-o."
　　　Alive, alive-o, alive, alive-o . . .

3　She died of a fever, and no one could save her,
　And that was the end of sweet Molly Malone,
　Now her ghost wheels her barrow through streets broad
　　　and narrow,
　Crying, "Cockles and mussels, alive, alive-o."
　　　Alive, alive-o, alive, alive-o . . .

Over the hills and far away

Not too fast

G   Em   Am7   D7   G   Em

1. Tom – he – was – a – pi – per's son, He learnt to – play – when –

Am7   D7   G   Em   Am

he was young, But all – the – tune – that – he could play Was

D7   Bm

"O – ver the hills and – far a – way." O – ver the hills and a

Em   Am   D7   1 Am7 D   2 Am7 D

great way off, The wind shall blow my top-knot off. top-knot off.

1   Tom, he was a piper's son,
He learnt to play when he was young,
But all the tune that he could play
Was "Over the hills and far away".
Over the hills and a great way off,
The wind will blow my top-knot off.

2   Tom with his pipe made such a noise,
That he pleased both the girls and boys,
And they all stopped to hear him play,
"Over the hills and far away".
Over the hills and a great way off,
The wind will blow my top-knot off.

3   Tom played his pipe with such good will
That those who heard him could ne'er keep still;
As soon as he played they began to dance,
E'en pigs on their hind legs began to prance.
Over the hills and a great way off,
The wind will blow my top-knot off.

4   Dolly was milking her cow one day,
Tom took out his pipe and began to play,
So Doll and the cow danced the "Cheshire Round"
Till the pail was broken and the milk
     ran on the ground.
Over the hills and a great way off,
The wind will blow my top-knot off.

Au clair de la lune

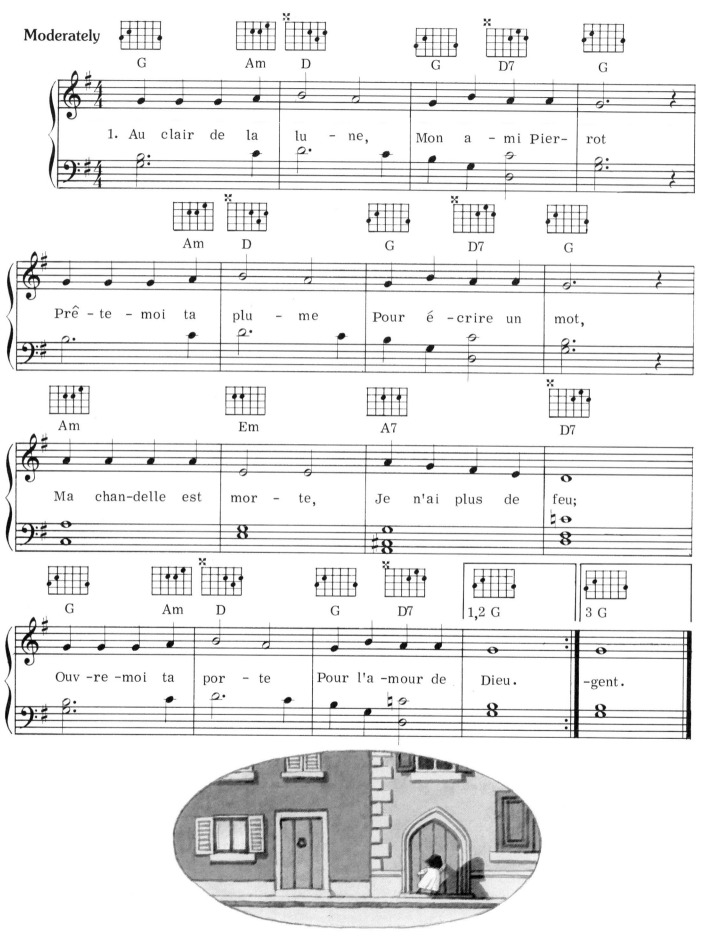

Moderately

G   Am   D   G   D7   G

1. Au clair de la lu - ne, Mon a - mi Pier - rot

Am   D   G   D7   G

Prê - te - moi ta plu - me Pour é - crire un mot,

Am   Em   A7   D7

Ma chan - delle est mor - te, Je n'ai plus de feu;

G   Am   D   G   D7   1,2 G   3 G

Ouv - re - moi ta por - te Pour l'a - mour de Dieu. -gent.

1 Au clair de la lune, mon ami Pierrot,
   Prête-moi ta plume, pour écrire un mot,
   Ma chandelle est morte, je n'ai plus de feu;
   Ouvre-moi ta porte, pour l'amour de Dieu.

2 Au clair de la lune Pierrot répondit:
   Je n'ai pas de plume, je suis dans mon lit.
   Va chez la voisine, je crois qu'elle y est,
   Car, dans sa cuisine, on bat le briquet.

3 Au clair de la lune Pierrot se rendort,
   Il rêve à la lune, son coeur bat bien fort:
   Car toujours si bonne pour l'enfant tout blanc,
   La lune lui donne son croissant d'argent.

Aiken Drum

Brightly

1. There__ was a man lived__ in the moon, lived in the moon, lived

in the moon, There was a man__ lived__ in the moon, And his name was Ai-ken

Drum; And he played up-on a__ la - dle, a la - dle a

la - dle, And he played up-on__ a__ la - dle, And his

name was Ai-ken Drum. 2. And his Drum.

1 There was a man lived in the moon,
      lived in the moon, lived in the moon,
There was a man lived in the moon,
And his name was Aiken Drum;
   And he played upon a ladle, a ladle, a ladle,
   And he played upon a ladle,
   And his name was Aiken Drum.

2 And his hat was made of good cream cheese,
      good cream cheese, good cream cheese,
And his hat was made of good cream cheese,
And his name was Aiken Drum.

   And he played upon a ladle, a ladle, a ladle . . .

3 And his coat was made of good roast beef,
      good roast beef, good roast beef,
And his coat was made of good roast beef,
And his name was Aiken Drum.

   And he played upon a ladle, a ladle, a ladle . . .

4 And his buttons were made of penny loaves,
      penny loaves, penny loaves,
And his buttons were made of penny loaves,
And his name was Aiken Drum.

   And he played upon a ladle, a ladle, a ladle . . .

5 His waistcoat was made of crust of pies,
      crust of pies, crust of pies,
His waistcoat was made of crust of pies,
And his name was Aiken Drum.

   And he played upon a ladle, a ladle, a ladle . . .

Strawberry Fair

As I was going to Strawberry Fair,
Singing, singing buttercups and daisies,
I met a maiden selling her ware,
Fol-de-dee.
I met a maiden selling her ware
As she went on to Strawberry Fair.

　　Rifol, rifol, tol-de-riddle-lido,
　　Rifol, rifol, tol-de-riddle-dee.

As I was going to Strawberry Fair,
Singing, singing hollyhocks and roses,
I met a farmer leading his mare,
Fol-de-dee.
I met a farmer leading his mare
As he went down to Strawberry Fair.

　　Rifol, rifol, tol-de-riddle-lido,
　　Rifol, rifol, tol-de-riddle-dee.

As I was going to Strawberry Fair,
Singing, singing meadowsweet and clover,
I met a bishop saying a prayer,
Fol-de-dee.
I met a bishop saying a prayer
As he went down to Strawberry Fair.

　　Rifol, rifol, tol-de-riddle-lido,
　　Rifol, rifol, tol-de-riddle-dee.

51

Oh, Susanna

Steadily

1. I__ came from Al - a - bam - a With my ban - jo on my knee; I'm__ goin' to Louis - i - an - a, My true love for to see. It__ rained all night the day I left, The weath-er it was

1 I come from Alabama
   With my banjo on my knee;
   I'm going to Louisiana,
   My true love for to see.
   It rained all night the day I left,
   The weather it was dry,
   The sun so hot I froze to death,
   Susanna, don't you cry.

Oh, Susanna,
Oh, don't you cry for me.
I've come from Alabama
With my banjo on my knee.

dry, The__ sun so hot I froze to death, Sus- an -na, don't you

cry. Oh, Sus- an -na, Oh don't you cry for me. I've__

come from Al-a - bam-a With my ban-jo on my knee. 2.I__ knee.

2 I had a dream the other night
   When everything was still;
   I thought I saw Susanna
   A-coming down the hill.
   The buckwheat cake was in her mouth,
   A tear was in her eye;
   Says I, "I'm comin' from the South,
   Susanna, don't you cry."

      Oh, Susanna,
      Oh, don't you cry for me.
      I've come from Alabama
      With my banjo on my knee.

Michael, row the boat ashore

1   Michael, row the boat ashore, hallelujah.
    Michael, row the boat ashore, hallelujah.

2   Sister, help to trim the sail, hallelujah.
    Sister, help to trim the sail, hallelujah.

3   Brother, won't you lend a hand? Hallelujah.
    Steer us to the Promised Land, hallelujah.

4   Children, sing a happy song, hallelujah.
    Help to speed the boat along, hallelujah.

5   River Jordan's deep and wide, hallelujah.
    Milk and honey on the other side, hallelujah.

A froggy went a-courting

Steadily

F

1. A frog-gy went a-court-ing and he did ride, ah-hum, ah-

Gm C7 F

-hum, A frog-gy went a-court-ing and he did ride, ah-hum, ah-

Bb F

-hum, A frog-gy went a-court-ing and he did ride, Sword and pis-tol

Bb F G7

Gm7 F

by his side, ah - hum, ah - hum. 2. He

1-8 9

hum.

56

1 A froggy went a-courting and he did ride, ah-hum, ah-hum,
A froggy went a-courting and he did ride, ah-hum, ah-hum,
A froggy went a-courting and he did ride,
Sword and pistol by his side, ah-hum, ah-hum.

2 He rode down to Missy Mouse's door, ah-hum, ah-hum,
He rode down to Missy Mouse's door, ah-hum, ah-hum,
He rode down to Missy Mouse's door,
Where he had been many times before, ah-hum, ah-hum.

3 He took Missy Mouse upon his knee, ah-hum, ah-hum . . .
Said, "Miss Mouse, will you marry me?" ah-hum, ah-hum.

4 "Without my Uncle Rat's consent," ah-hum, ah-hum . . .
"I wouldn't marry the President," oh-no, oh-no.

5 Uncle Rat laughed and shook his fat sides, ho-ho, ho-ho . . .
To think his niece would be a bride, ho-ho, ho-ho.

6 "Where will the wedding breakfast be?" er-hum, er-hum . . .
"Way down yonder in the hollow tree," er-hum- er-hum.

7 "What will the wedding breakfast be?" er-hum, er-hum . . .
"Fried mosquito and a black-eyed pea," yum-yum, yum-yum

8 They all went sailing across the lake, ah-hum, ah-hum . . .
And got swallowed by a big black snake, oh-no, oh-no.

9 There's bread and cheese upon the shelf, er-hum, er-hum . . .
If you want any more, you can sing it yourself, er-hum, er-hum.

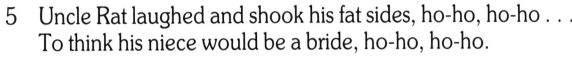

Home, home on the range

1 Oh, give me a home where the buffalo roam,
   Where the deer and the antelope play,
   Where seldom is heard a discouraging word,
   And the sky is not cloudy or grey.

   Home, home on the range.
   Where the deer and the antelope play,
   Where seldom is heard
      a discouraging word,
   And the sky is not cloudy or grey.

2   Oh, give me a gale in some soft Southern vale,
Where the stream of life joyfully flows,
On the banks of the river, where seldom if ever,
Any poisonous herb-i-age grows.

     Home, home on the range . . .

3   Oh, give me a land where the bright diamond sands
Lie awash in the glittering stream,
Where days glide along in pleasure and song,
And afternoons pass as a dream.

     Home, home on the range . . .

Donkey riding

Brightly

D   G   D   A

1. Were you ev - er in Que - bec Stow - ing car - go on the deck?

D   G   D   A7   D

There's the king with a gold - en crown Rid - ing on a don - key.

G   D   A7   D   A

Hey, ho, a - way we go, Don - key rid - ing, don - key rid - ing,

G   D   A7   D   A7   1,2. D   3. D

Hey, ho, a - way we go, Rid - ing on a don - key. don - key.

60

1   Were you ever in Quebec,
    Stowing cargo on the deck?
    There's the king with a golden crown,
    Riding on a donkey.

        Hey, ho, away we go,
        Donkey riding, donkey riding,
        Hey, ho, away we go,
        Riding on a donkey.

2   Were you ever off Cape Horn,
    Where it's always fine and warm,
    And seen the lion and the unicorn
    Riding on a donkey?

        Hey, ho, away we go . . .

3   Were you ever in Cardiff Bay,
    Where the folks all shout, "Hurray!
    Here comes John with his three years' pay
    Riding on a donkey?"

        Hey, ho, away we go . . .

Lewis Wedding Song

Lively

G — C — G

Step we gai - ly, on we go, Heel for heel and toe for toe,

C — G — *Fine*

Arm in arm and row on row, All for Mai - ri's wed - ding.

G — C — G

1. O - ver hill - ways, up and down, Myr - tle green and brack - en brown,

C — 1,2 G *D.C.* — 3 G *D.C. al Fine*

Past the shie - lings, through the town, All for sake of Mai - ri. Mai - ri.

Step we gaily, on we go,
Heel for heel and toe for toe,
Arm in arm and row on row,
All for Mairi's wedding.

1   Over hillways up and down,
    Myrtle green and bracken brown,
    Past the shielings, through the town;
    All for sake of Mairi.

        Step we gaily, on we go . . .

2   Red her cheeks as rowans are,
    Bright her eye as any star,
    Fairest of them all by far,
    Is our darling Mairi.

        Step we gaily, on we go . . .

3   Plenty herring, plenty meal,
    Plenty peat to fill her creel,
    Plenty bonnie bairns as weel;
    That's the toast for Mairi.

        Step we gaily, on we go . . .

Shieling is the Scottish word for summer pastures, creel is a basket, and bairns are children.

Index of first lines

A froggy went a-courting and he did ride, 56
As I was going to Strawberry Fair, 50
Au clair de la lune, 46
Dashing through the snow, 22
Down by the pen, there the old shearer stands, 34
Frère Jacques, Frère Jacques, 17
Half a pound of tuppenny rice, 30
Here we go round the mulberry bush, 4
I come from Alabama with my banjo on my knee, 52
I had a little nut tree, 16
I saw three ships come sailing by, 26
If you're happy and you know it, 8
In Dublin's fair city, where girls are so pretty, 42
Little Bo Peep, she lost her sheep, 7
London Bridge is falling down, 28
Michael, row the boat ashore, 54
My bonnie lies over the ocean, 36
Oh, give me a home where the buffalo roam, 58
Oh, the grand old Duke of York, 31
Old MacDonald had a farm, 14
One, two, three, four, five, once I caught a fish alive, 6
She'll be coming round the mountain, 38
Sing a song of sixpence, 20
Step we gaily, on we go, 62
The animals went in one by one, 32
There was a man lived in the moon, 48
There was an old man named Michael Finnigan, 24
There were ten in the bed, 10
There's a big ship sailing on the illy-ally-o, 40
This old man, he played one, 18
Tom, he was a piper's son, 44
Twinkle, twinkle, little star, 12
Were you ever in Quebec? 60
Where, oh where has my little dog gone? 9
Yankee Doodle came to town, 27